C is for CAT with her soft, silky fur.
Just feed her and stroke her.
I'm sure she will purr.

D is for DOG with a loud, happy bark.
I ~~love to go~~ "walkies" and play ~~in~~ the park.

G for GIRAFFE. See him nibble, with ease,
The tastiest leaves at the tops of the trees.

H for the fat baby HIPPOPOTAMUS.
He lies in his mud bath and
grins out at us

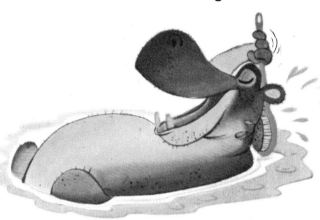

K is for KANGAROO. She is no slouch,
As she bounds around with her babe
in her pouch.

L is for LION. With his thunderous roar,
You'd think this big animal's throat
would get sore!

Throat
Tablets

80p

Now take a look at the back of the book.

The Bimbo BOOK

1978

Printed and Published by D. C. Thomson & Co., Ltd., Dundee and London.

A Letter From Bimbo

Dear 👧👧 and 👦👦👦,

    Here is another bright and colourful **BIMBO BOOK** for you.

    Lots of your chums are inside to greet you.... Baby Crockett, Pip the Penguin and Milly the Mermaid

    You will enjoy the super stories about The Little Lorry, The Bottle Imp and The Old Armchair.

    And the many **PUZZLES** will keep you busy on a rainy day.

Bye-bye for now,

Bimbo

Pam goes shopping

Young Bimbo's going with Pam, his chum,
To do some shopping for his mum.

They buy some buttons, string and eggs.
Buckets, coat hangers and clothes pegs.

There's lots to carry, as you see.
Then Bimbo says, "Leave this to me!"

He's pegged the shopping up. Hooray!
It's easily carried home that way!

Teggy Taggle-tail

"COME along," quacked Mrs Taggle-tail to her three little ducklings, Tiggy, Toggy, and Teggy. "Today, I am going to teach you to swim. Then you can have fun."

She waddled off to the pond. Tiggy and Toggy followed close behind.

But Teggy thought he would look around and find out what everyone else was doing. Perhaps he would find something to do that was more fun than swimming.

2 — Teggy scrambled through a hedge into a field. There, he met Mrs Hare and her family.

"Hello!" said Teggy Taggle-tail, with a friendly smile. "What are you teaching your family today?" he asked Mrs Hare politely.

"I am showing them how to run," Mrs Hare told him. "Then they can have lots of fun racing through the fields and woods."

"Please, will you also teach me?" asked Teggy Taggle-tail.

"All right," said Mrs Hare. "Go and stand beside the others. When I say 'Go!' you must race across the fields and into Hickory Wood."

3 — "Ready! Steady! Go!" called out Mrs Hare.

The little hares pushed hard with their long back legs and off they went. All except poor Teggy Taggle-tail! He was soon left behind! His webbed feet got all tangled up and he fell over, hurting his toes.

"Bother!" he said, as he rubbed his toes sadly.

4 — Teggy waddled on. He soon cheered up when he met Mrs Swallow and her family.

"Hello," said Teggy Taggle-tail. "What are you teaching your family today?" he asked.

"They're learning to fly," said Mrs Swallow. "Then, when it grows cold, they can fly across the sea to follow the sunshine."

"Please, will you teach me to fly?" asked Teggy.

"I'll try," said Mrs Swallow. "First, flap your wings to make them strong." They all flapped their wings. "Now, follow me!" she cried.

5 — Mrs Swallow flew into the sky. All the young swallows flew up behind her. Poor Teggy Taggle-tail was soon left behind. He tried to flap his wings harder and jump into the air. But, *plop*! He fell right down again on to his nose.

Sadly, he watched the Swallow family fly away, high in the sky.

"I can't do *anything*," he sighed.

Teggy cheered up when he met Mrs Blackbird and her family.

6 — "What are you teaching your family?" he asked.

"I'm trying to make them sing. Then they can cheer up everyone," she said.

"Please, teach me to sing," said Teggy.

"Very well," said Mrs Blackbird, doubtfully. "Now, heads up. Sing, after me, doh, ray, me."

Everyone sang "Doh, ray, me," — except Teggy! He could only go "Quack, quack, quack!" The blackbirds flew away in fright.

7 — This time, Teggy Taggle-tail didn't cheer up.

"What is the matter?" asked Mrs Owl, kindly.

Teggy looked up at her and a big tear ran down his beak. "I can't run like a hare, I can't fly like a swallow and I can't sing!" he sighed.

Mrs Owl hooted with laughter. "Of course you can't. You're a *duck* — and ducks *swim*! Now, off you go to the pond."

8 — So, Teggy waddled along to the pond. There, he saw his mother, Tiggy and Toggy swimming around happily.

"Come along in," called his mother.

Teggy went into the water. In no time at all he, too, was swimming.

"Why, I am quite clever after all," thought the little duck to himself.

His mother watched proudly. Teggy Taggle-tail had at last found out it was much more fun doing what a little duck *should* do!

The Little Lorry

1 — Mike was a little lorry. He lived in a cosy wooden garage in a big forest. Mike drove along the forest tracks every day, carrying piles of logs to the sawmill.

2 — The animals who lived among the trees liked Mike, because he was always cheerful. Every morning, Mike called "Good morning" to his chums.

3 — Then, with a *vroom, vroom*! the little lorry trundled out of his garage home. He sped off to work, waving his wipers as he passed his friends.

4 — Mike's chum, Bertie Bulldozer, had already started work. "Good morning, Mike," Bertie puffed. Bertie wasn't very clever, but he was ever so strong!

5 — Mike worked hard all day. The crane on his back swung round, picked up logs and set them down behind the cab. Then Mike took the logs to the sawmill.

6 — The sun was setting before the little lorry stopped work. As Mike sped home, he tooted "Goodnight" to the animals.

7 — The Squirrel family was getting ready for bed, too. They lived in a hollow tree trunk beside the river. "Goodnight," called Mike, flashing his lights.

8 — In the middle of the night, Mike was wakened by a raging storm. "Bless my nuts and bolts! I'm glad I'm safely in my warm garage!" thought Mike.

9 — Next morning, just as Mike was leaving for work, Blinky Owl fluttered down in front of him. "Come quickly, Mike!" he hooted. "The Squirrels' home was swept into the river!"

10 — Mike's engine roared into life. His wheels had never spun round so quickly, as he drove along the path at top speed!

11 — Mike could see the Squirrel family from the river bank. They were seated on their hollow log, drifting downstream. "Please save us!" called Mrs Squirrel.

12 — The little lorry screeched to a stop on the bridge which crossed the river. He lowered his crane and waited. Soon, the Squirrels reached the bridge.

13 — Quickly, Mike hooked his crane on to the log. "Hold tightly, now," he tooted. Then he lifted the log out of the water and pulled the Squirrels to safety.

14 — Mike didn't even let the Squirrels say "thank you". He just made sure they were all right before he sped off. You see, he didn't want to be late for work!

15 — However, that evening, the Squirrels *did* thank Mike. They held a party specially for him. Every animal in the forest was there.

16 — "Three cheers for Mike! He's the best lorry in the world!" called Mr Squirrel. Mike blushed from the top of his cab to the bottom of his tyres!

Debby (and the) Donkey

TIMOTHY was one of Mr Stubbs' beach donkeys. Mr Stubbs had five other donkeys besides Timothy, but Timothy was the oldest. All day long, the donkeys gave rides to children.

Many of the children were kind and gentle with the donkeys. Others pulled their manes and ears.

2 — Timothy knew that the children didn't mean to hurt him.

"They just don't know how to treat a donkey," he thought. "And I'm getting too old for this. When I was younger, it didn't bother me so much."

Then another little boy came for a donkey ride. He held on so tightly to the reins that poor Timothy's jaws were aching!

"I don't know how I shall ever stand another summer of this," thought Timothy.

3 — Timothy's first customer, after lunch, was a little girl.

"Hello," she said shyly. "My name is Debby. Mr Stubbs tells me you are called Timothy."

Timothy liked Debby at once.

"I'm sure she won't tug," he said to himself.

Timothy was right. Debby was very gentle. She even gave him some sugar lumps when she finished her ride.

4 — Every day after that, Debby came to the beach. She always had a donkey ride — on Timothy, of course. As Timothy plodded across the sands, Debby would speak to him. She told him all about the farm where she lived. Timothy thought it sounded lovely.

One day, after her ride, Debby suddenly gave Timothy a big hug.

"I'm going home tomorrow, Timothy," she said. "So I must say good-bye now."

Timothy was sadder than he had ever been in his life!

5 — Next morning, when the sun came up, Mr Stubbs led his donkeys out of their stable — all except for Timothy. The donkey couldn't understand it. He watched as his chums clattered out of the yard on their way to the beach.

"I wonder why I've been left behind?" thought Timothy. "I'm not ill, or anything."

Poor Timothy couldn't think of a single reason why he had not been taken to the beach!

6 — Later that morning, a horse-box was driven into the stable yard. It stopped beside Timothy's stall. Then the driver led Timothy out into the yard.

"Come on, old man," said the driver. "Up you go, into the horse-box."

Timothy was even more puzzled by this.

7 — Timothy went on a long journey in the horse-box. He was driven through town after town, village after village. He didn't know where he was going. The journey was taking him further and further away from the sea-side.

At last, the horse-box was driven through some gates. Then it stopped. The next thing Timothy heard was a voice he knew very well — Debby's!

"Welcome to your new home, Timothy," she said. "I liked you so much on holiday that I couldn't bear to be parted from you. So Daddy bought you from Mr Stubbs. Now you are going to stay with us for ever."

8 —- Debby led Timothy to a field behind the farmhouse.

"This is your field, Timothy," she said.

Timothy was delighted. It was a very nice field, with a comfy little stable in one corner.

Timothy felt so happy that he galloped round the field and kicked his hoofs in the air. Debby laughed and laughed.

"I'm so glad you've come to stay with us, Timothy," she said. "I know you're going to be happy."

The Old Armchair

D^O *you* have an old armchair? The Jackson family owned one. Their armchair was old and shabby. But it was so large and comfy, *everybody* loved to sit in it.

Each evening, after tea, Mr Jackson sank down into the chair. The children, John and Sally, played on its wide arms, while Pussy snoozed on the chair's big back.

The comfy, old chair then sighed contentedly. It loved being sat on.

2 — The Jackson family also had some shiny, new, modern furniture in their house.

"Why do you like being sat on?" the modern furniture asked the old chair, one night.

"People give me presents!" the chair said.

"Presents? What nonsense!" cried the skinny lampshade.

"Silly thing!" sneered a spindly new chair.

But the old chair would only smile.

3 — One day, the Jacksons decided to spring-clean their house.

They covered up all the furniture with dust sheets.

They re-painted their living room. Then they dusted and cleaned, until the house sparkled. At last, Mr Jackson pulled the dust covers from the furniture. But, now, the old chair looked shabbier than ever.

"That chair will have to go!" cried Mr Jackson.

4 — "Oh, no! Not our dear, old chair!" wailed Mrs Jackson. "I'll give it a good clean. That will make it look better."

She removed all the cushions. As she patted the cover in place, Mrs Jackson felt something down the side.

"Look! It's my locket!" she called out.

"Well, well. Perhaps my missing pen is there, too!" said Mr Jackson.

Sure enough, Mr Jackson's lost pen was wedged behind the seat.

In no time, other members of the family found little lost treasures, too.

5 — "I've found my comb!" cried Cousin Liz.

"And here's that photograph I lost," cried Grandma Jackson. The comfy, old chair had something for *everybody*!

6 — At last, all was quiet.

"That old chair *does* give presents to people," the lampshade whispered.

"No wonder he's so popular," sighed the book-case.

"It's just as nice to give presents as it is to receive them," murmured the old chair.

He chuckled quietly to himself and settled down for a snooze.

Well, after that, the Jackson family agreed that they would *never* ever part with their comfy, old chair.

Puzzle Play-time

Shade in the dotted shapes to see an animal which cowboys and Indians hunted at one time.

Which two of Big Chief Teddy Bear's feathers are exactly the same?

Which one of these little bears has lassoed the calf?

A

B

C

A Picture To Paint.

There are eight differences between these two Indians and their canoes. Can you spot them?

Can you find a cup, a fish, a trumpet, an apple, a book, a wine glass, an arrow, a lemon and a key hidden in this picture?

Pip the Penguin

"What's wrong?" asks Pip when he meets a sad, little deer.

The reindeer wants antlers like the grown-up deer.

So, Pip buys an old set of antlers from the nearby store.

Then he ties them on to the baby deer's head.

But the big antlers make the deer bump into two trees.

Next moment, a pile of snow falls down on top of the poor deer.

Then he knocks over a bird perch with the clumsy antlers.

The perch is broken. How sorry the little deer feels.

But Pip knows what to do. He unties the antlers . . .

. . . and uses them to make a super new perch for the birds.

The baby deer feels better without the antlers, anyway!

The B[ttle Imp

1 — One day, a boy called Jerry went down to the harbour. An old sailing ship was anchored there, and Jerry wanted to make sketches of it. He hoped to do a drawing of the ship.

2 — Suddenly, Jerry saw a strange, old bottle bobbing about in the water. Using a boat hook, he fished out the bottle.

3 — "I wonder what is inside," he thought, excitedly. "Perhaps someone put a note in it. It could have come from the other side of the world!"

4 — Jerry tugged at the stopper. It was stiff, but, at last, *whoosh!* — out it popped. The boy was so startled that he didn't see something whizzing into the air.

5 — "Hello, there," said a little voice. "W-what — w-who's that?" cried Jerry, looking round in surprise. "Up here, silly!" said the voice.

6 — Suddenly, a little figure appeared before Jerry's eyes. It was swinging from his hair. "Who are *you*?" gasped Jerry. "Where are you from?"

7 — "I am an Imp. I was imprisoned in the bottle by a wicked wizard and I've been there, asleep, for hundreds of years," explained the Imp.

8 — Well, the Imp stayed with Jerry. A few days later, the boy was working on his sailing ship while his mummy was tidying up. "This old bottle can go out," she said.

9 — Jerry watched with dismay as Mum threw the bottle, with the Imp inside, into the dustbin. When his mother had gone, Jerry rushed out.

10 — Very carefully, he lifted the Imp out of the bin. "Oo! Ow! I must be bruised all over! What did your mum want to do that for?" cried the tiny fellow.

11 — Jerry brought the Imp inside and settled down to work again. However, the Imp was bored. Then he saw Jerry's dog falling asleep on the floor.

12 — He lifted the dog's ear. "Hello!" he called. *"Wo-ooo!"* howled the dog, in surprise. "Don't tease Rover," cried Jerry, trying to calm down the dog.

13 — Soon, Jerry had finished making his model sailing ship. He popped it into a pretty bottle and tried to raise the masts by pulling a thread.

14 — But, oh dear! The thread snapped! "Now, what will I do? I can't get the ship out again," cried Jerry. "I'll help," said the Imp. He jumped inside the bottle.

15 — Well, the little fellow soon had all the masts standing upright. "I think I'll make this my home," he said. "I like it here."

16 — "Ho-ho! Mum wouldn't throw out *this* bottle and Rover won't find you here," laughed Jerry. "And a ship in a bottle is just right for a Bottle Imp," said his tiny pal.

1 — One day, Baby is in town with Mum. He stops at a music shop window. "I'd like to play a musical instrument," he sighs. Mum *is* pleased.

4 — Baby doesn't give up. He tries to play the trumpet. He blows and blows, but he can't make a sound!

5—Mr Louden, Baby's next teacher, gives lessons on the double bass. "Phew!" puffs Baby. "This instrument is too heavy for me!"

8 — Later, Baby dresses neatly. "I'm going for a music lesson," he tells Mum.

9 — "Who is your teacher?" asks Mrs Crockett. "You've been to all the teachers in town!" Baby points to Linda's gate.

2 — Next day, she takes our little chum to see Miss Key who gives piano lessons.

3 — However, Baby can't reach the piano keys from the stool. He is too small! "Bring him back in a few years," says the teacher.

6 — The next teacher that Baby visits plays the accordion. However, it is as big as the little lad!

7 — On the way home, Baby meets Linda. "Why are you so glum?" she asks. Baby tells her the sad story.

10 — On it is a sign saying, 'Linda. Music Teacher" "Ho-ho!" chuckles Mum.

11 — Linda has brought out her toy piano for Baby. Mrs Crockett watches, while the little girl teaches her "pupil". Baby likes *this* lesson!

Milly the Mermaid

AT the bottom of the sea there is a super place called Deepdown Land. That is where a pretty, little mermaid called Milly lives . . .

One day, Milly and two of her chums, Billy and Bobby, the shrimp twins, went to see Wally Walrus. Wally owned the Sea-bed Tea Shop. While they were there, a storm sprang up. The water swirled and swooshed all around the tea shop.

2 — "I've never seen such a storm in Deepdown Land," said Milly, as she rushed to the door.

"Don't go out, Billy and Bobby. You'll get knocked down," she added, as her chums darted forward.

"Oh, dear!" cried Wally. "Is it really as bad as that? I must bring in the tables and chairs from outside."

However, he was too late. The water current was so strong that the cafe furniture was being tossed around the place.

All poor Wally could do was stand and watch as the tables and chairs were broken and smashed and holes were torn in the bright umbrellas.

3 — At last, the storm passed. Wally rushed out to look at the damaged furniture.

"It's all ruined!" he sighed. "I'll never be able to mend it and I don't have enough money to buy new things. I'll have to close my tea shop."

"Please, Wally. Don't be upset," said Milly kindly. "I'm sure something will turn up."

"You're just saying that to cheer me up," said Wally. He shook his head sadly and wandered back inside.

4 — Billy and Bobby asked Milly to play with them.

"We know where there is a wrecked ship," said Bobby. "It's a super place for playing at hide and seek."

Some anchors and barrels lay around the wreck.

"Will you fetch some of your chums?" Milly asked the shrimps. "I know how we can help Wally."

5 — Soon, lots of other little shrimps arrived. They brought a large hand-barrow.

"Now load the barrels and anchors on to the cart and follow me," said Milly.

"How can these things help Wally?" wondered Billy.

6 — Well, Billy soon found out! When they reached the tea shop, Milly explained how the big barrels could be tables and the small barrels made into chairs.

"And I think the anchors can be fixed to hold up clam shells to make umbrellas," she added.

So, the shrimps set to work with hammers and nails and, before long, they had made Wally's tea shop look just as good as new.

"Now you can keep your tea shop open," laughed Milly. "And it hasn't cost you a penny, either."

"You and your hard working chums must be my first customers, Milly," said Wally.

"Or should I say 'guests'! You see, to thank you, I'm going to give you all a grand afternoon tea of lemonade, ice-cream and cakes."

And that is just what Wally did!

"Jingles"

THEY call me Jingles
For every time
I start to speak,
I speak in rhyme.

A is for April,
　　With sunshine and showers
To swell the trees' buds
　　And awaken the flowers.

P is for Primroses,
　　Down in the glade.
I've picked some. And look at
　　The bonnet I've made!

R is for Rabbits.
　　I DO think they're funny.
I've brought bits of lettuce
　　For each baby bunny!

I is for Irises,
　　Slender and blue.
I'll take some to Mummy,
　　And Aunt Mary, too.

L is for Lapwings,
　　And Linnets and Larks,
All building their nests
　　In the woodlands and parks.

The Cheery Chicks

THE four Cheery Chicks lived on a farm. The three yellow chicks were called Eeny, Meeny and Miny, while the little black chick was called Mo.

One day, Eeny saw the farmer's son, Tommy, and his friends getting ready to go on a hike.

"I would also like to go hiking," thought Eeny. He scampered off to look for the other Cheery Chicks.

2 — At last he found Meeny, Miny and Mo playing in a meadow near the farm.

"Tommy is going hiking with his friends," Eeny cheeped.

"That sounds fun," chirped Mo. "I've always wanted to see the countryside."

"Let's invite *our* friends to come hiking with us, too," cried Eeny.

The Cheery Chicks scampered off in all directions to call on their animal chums.

3 — A family of bunnies lived in a burrow on the edge of the meadow.

"Coo-ee!" called Eeny, as he popped his head down the rabbit hole. His three bunny chums appeared.

"We're all going hiking," said Eeny. "Come with us."

"Not today," replied Bobby Bunny. "We're just finishing lunch. We're going to have a nap now."

"Sleepyheads!" Eeny called, as he waddled away.

"Now, who else can I call on," he thought to himself. Then he saw the duck pond in the distance.

"I'll call on Daisy Duck," he went on.

4 — Daisy Duck was swimming round the pond with her family of four fluffy ducklings.

"How would you like a nice, long walk," cheeped Eeny.

"A nice, long walk? Oh, no!" quacked Daisy Duck loudly.

"You see, I'm going hiking with my brothers," said Eeny. "We thought it would be fun if all the farmyard animals came with us!"

"I'm not taking my children for a walk on *dry land*!" Daisy quacked, even louder. "We don't want to leave our nice, wet pond. *Swimming* is more fun than *walking*!"

So, Eeny went off to join Meeny, Miny and Mo.

5 — "Nobody wants to go hiking with us," cheeped Mo, when Eeny came along.

"Ho-hum!" yawned Eeny. "I'm tired after chasing all over the farmyard. I think I'll have a nap instead."

"What a good idea," cheeped Mo. "I feel sleepy, too."

The Cheery Chicks looked for somewhere cosy to sleep. Mo spotted a rucksack lying on the farmhouse doorstep. There were four neat, little pockets on the front of the bag.

"Climb in. There's room for everybody," Eeny called sleepily.

The Cheery Chicks snuggled down in the four little pockets in the rucksack. Soon, they all fell fast asleep.

6 — When they woke up, they were on the move!

You see, Tommy had taken the rucksack when he went hiking.

He didn't know the Cheery Chicks were inside it — asleep!

"I see you went on a hike after all," called Bobby Bunny. "All the walking you sleepy-heads could have done, though, would be in your *dreams*!"

How to make
Bunty Butterfly

by **Bimbo**

COLOUR two corks and join them together with a used matchstick, as the picture shows. This will make the butterfly's body. Crumple a piece of kitchen foil into a ball to form the head. Fix this to one of the corks with another used match. Push two more used matchsticks into the head for feelers.

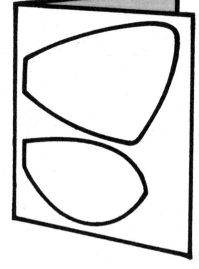

Draw two wings on a piece of thin cardboard that is folded in half. Cut out both layers of cardboard to make two pairs of wings. Colour the wings with bright patterns.

Ask Mummy or Daddy to make two cuts on opposite sides of one of the corks and then you can push the wings into these slots. If you like, you can hang Bunty from the ceiling by thread.

The Magic Pen

PATSY PETAL was a pixie at the Dreamy-time Nursery School. Patsy liked school, except for the writing lessons. You see, Patsy's writing was terrible! Somehow, her O's were always flattened, her S's were back to front and there were ink blots everywhere!

Each day, Miss Bloom, the teacher, decided who was the best writer. Then everyone in the class stood up and clapped their hands for that pupil.

Patsy was the only one in the class who had never earned a clap!

"Perhaps, if I try extra hard, I'll win a clap before we go on holiday," thought Patsy.

But her writing was just as bad.

2 — Then, one morning, Bettina Blossom and Fenella Fearn, Patsy's two best friends, saw how sad she looked.

"We must do something to help Patsy," said Bettina. "We'll go and ask the Wizard-as-old-as-time."

"Oh!" gasped Fenella. "He lives so far away. We would have to go through The Enchanted Wood, then across Moonbeam Lake, through the Valley of Violets and up the Mountain of Secrets."

"If we want to help Patsy, we must go," said Bettina bravely.

So, the two chums set off on their adventure.

3 — Soon, they saw the dark branches of
The Enchanted Wood ahead of them.

"How will we ever find our way through the
wood?" cried Fenella.

Just then, a large, white rabbit appeared.

"Climb on my back, little ones. I will take you
through the wood," said the animal.

Before long, the rabbit set them down.

And there, stretching out in front of them,
was Moonbeam Lake.

"How are we going to cross?" sighed Fenella.

4 — "Climb on my back and I will take you
over the lake," said a lovely voice.

The pixies saw the most beautiful
swan. They sat on his downy feathers and were
carried swiftly across the lake.

Then the pixies walked across the perfumed
Valley of Violets. After a long time, they
reached the foot of the Mountain of Secrets.

"I will take you up to the wizard's cave,"
said a white goat that suddenly appeared.

Well, Bettina and Fenella were quite scared
when they looked into the cave.

"Come in, my dears," said the Wizard-as-
old-as-time. "Do not be afraid. I know many
things and have just the pen to help your
friend, Patsy."

5 — Well, the pixies were amazed! How did the wizard know all about Patsy!

"Take this pen to your friend. It will write as neatly as Patsy believes it will," said the wizard.

Then he clapped his hands and the white goat appeared again. The animal carried them back down the mountain.

Next day, Bettina and Fenella gave the magic pen to Patsy.

"Oh, it's a lovely pen!" cried Patsy. "I'm sure I can write well with this."

And do you know — she *did!*

6 — Miss Bloom collected all the exercise books and Patsy could hardly wait till the teacher had read them all.

Then came the announcement.

"The best writer today is Patsy!" said Miss Bloom.

"Hurrah!" cried all the little pixies. They stood up and clapped.

7 — In his cave at the top of the Mountain of Secrets, the Wizard-as-old-as-time soon knew that Patsy had won a clap. He always knew everything, you see. The wizard smiled to himself, knowing that the pen he had sent Patsy only became "magic" when she believed in it. Well, you know, that is how most magic works!

As the Wizard-as-old-as-time says, "All sorts of wonderful things *can* happen when you really believe they *will* happen!"

Bimbo builds a Snowman

When Bimbo saw the snow one day,
He said, "Let's all go out to play."

He called his pets. Outside they ran
To help him build a big snowman.

Then Bimbo fetched a little spade.
And two big snowball shapes he made.

These made the body and the head.
"He'll need a hat," young Bimbo said.

"My cowboy hat," he cried, with glee,
"Suits this fine snowman — you'll agree!"

Then Puppy put a mouth in place,
Giving the snowman a nice face.

Bimbo!
Coo-ee!
Where can
he be?

Two round, brown buttons —
                giant size —
Were just right for the
                snowman's eyes.

At last, Bimbo came into view,
Covered in snow —
                a snowman, too!

The Tick

*T*ICK! *Tock!* Christopher lay in bed, looking sleepily at his clock. There was a picture of a little red train in the middle of the clock's face. The wheels went round with every *tick tock* of the clock, so Christopher called it The Tick Tock Train.

2 — Beside each number was a tiny station. The clock's little hand was pointing to the blue one at number seven, while the big hand pointed upwards to the yellow station right at the top — number twelve. So Christopher knew it was seven o'clock.

"Do you visit all the stations while I'm asleep, Teddy?" he chuckled.

What a surprise he had when a tiny voice answered him.

"Why don't you come along and find out, Christopher?" asked Teddy.

All at once, they were puffing along the track in The Tick Tock Train. Magically, Teddy and Christopher were the same size!

Tick Tock Train

3 — What a thrilling journey it was. The Tick Tock Train stopped at Eight o'Clock Station for his breakfast of coal and water. Then he bustled on again. They rushed through Nine o'Clock Station and Ten o'Clock Station, too.

4 — At Eleven o'Clock, lots of bears came aboard.
"They're going off on a picnic," smiled Teddy.
When the train stopped at Twelve o'Clock Station, the passengers left.

— Teddy led Christopher to the Three Bears' Cottage. Of course, they had some porridge!
When they left, Tick Tock whistled a merry tune.
Many stations later, the train stopped at Seven o'Clock Station.
"Goodnight, Christopher," yawned Teddy.
"Good *morning*!" cried Christopher. And then he woke up. Christopher's ride on The Tick Tock Train had been in his dreams!

Puzzle Play-time

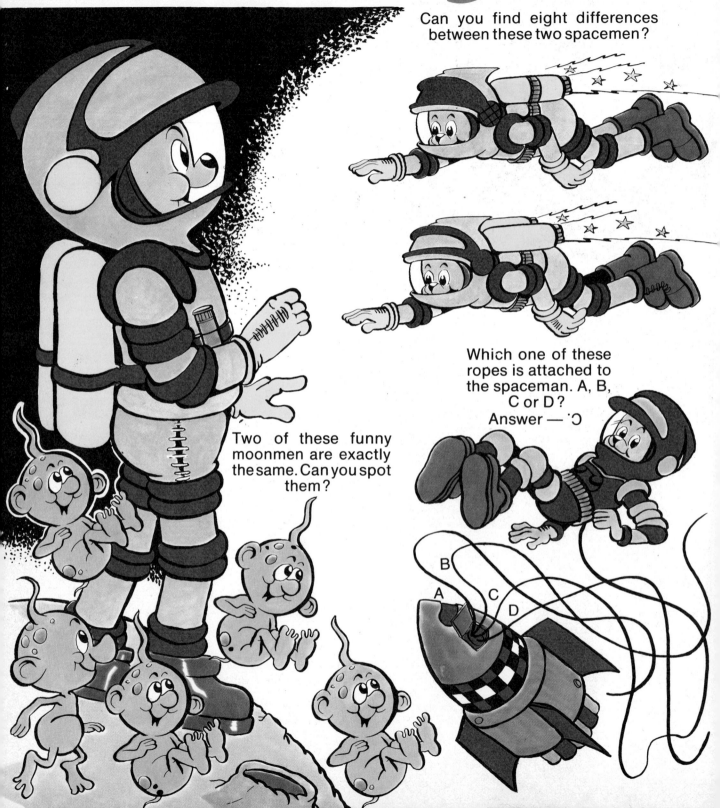

Can you find eight differences between these two spacemen?

Two of these funny moonmen are exactly the same. Can you spot them?

Which one of these ropes is attached to the spaceman. A, B, C or D?
Answer — C.

A Picture To Paint

Join the dots to find out what this spaceman used to travel to the moon.

Can you find a chess board, a yacht, a bottle, an arrow, a drawing pin, a bow-tie, a watch, a spoon and a bowl hidden in this picture?

Harvey's House

THIS little gnome is called Harvey. As you can see, Harvey has a most unusual house — an old top hat!

Harvey had found the hat once, sitting just where it was. He was looking for somewhere to stay at the time, so he decided there and then to make the top hat his home. He nailed it to the ground, made windows and a door and moved in.

In time, Harvey made a garden round his house. He kept the house and the garden very neat and tidy.

"I really am a lucky gnome to have such a lovely home," thought Harvey.

The little gnome didn't know it yet, but his luck was about to change!

2 — That night, a fierce storm blew up. The wind huffed and puffed round Harvey's house. Then it lifted the top hat off the ground and carried it far, far away. All Harvey's clothes and things were blown away, too. Harvey was sleeping so soundly, he didn't know anything had happened.

3 — You can guess how dismayed Harvey was next morning when he found that his house was gone.

"My lovely little home!" sobbed the gnome. "Whatever will I do now?"

There was only one thing Harvey could do. He had to find a new house. He packed his few belongings in a spotted handkerchief and set off.

Harvey didn't know where he might find somewhere to stay, so he just walked along the first road he came to. Soon, he reached a warren of rabbit burrows.

"Perhaps I could stay here," he thought.

4 — Harvey knocked on one of the doors— *rat-a-tat*! The door was opened by a rabbit in an apron.

"My house was blown away by the wind last night," said Harvey. "I'm looking for a new home."

"Well, you can't stay here," said Mrs Bunny. "I have ten children. There are too many of us in this burrow as it is. I'm sorry, but we don't have an inch to spare for anyone else."

5 — Harvey trudged along the road again. At last, he reached a town. The motor cars which thundered past frightened Harvey, so he turned into a quiet lane. The lane was full of dustbins, old boxes and all sorts of rubbish.

"It may be quiet, but it isn't very nice," thought Harvey.

Then Harvey had to take cover in an old box, as a big, ginger pussy cat stalked past.

"I've never met a pussy cat before," sighed Harvey. "I don't know whether they are kind to little gnomes or not!"

6 — By now it was dark, so Harvey decided to spend the night in a cardboard box. He found a piece of newspaper to use as a blanket and curled up to go to sleep.

But Harvey couldn't sleep. It soon started to rain and the cardboard box leaked. Water dripped down on the little gnome's head.

"I can't stay here," said Harvey.

7 — So, Harvey left the cardboard box. Just then, the gnome saw a hole between two planks of wood.

"What's in there?" he muttered.

Well, there was only one way to find out! Harvey walked through the hole and found himself in a toy shop!

8 — A big baby doll spoke to Harvey.

"Who are you?" she asked. "What are you doing here?"

"I'm Harvey," said the little gnome. "My house was blown away in a storm last night. I've been wandering around all day, looking for a new home, but I haven't found one. I'm so cold and tired now, and I don't know where to go next!"

"You can go in there," said the doll, pointing to a pretty doll's house.

Harvey could hardly believe it.

"Can I really?" he asked.

"Of course you can," said the baby doll. "You'll feel much better tomorrow, after a good night's rest."

9 — Harvey opened the doll's house door and went inside.

"This house is just the right size for me," he cried. "The chairs and tables are my height and it's so warm and snug! What a pity I can't stay here always!"

Then Harvey found the bedroom. In no time at all, he was tucked up cosily under the blankets. A few moments later, when the baby doll peeped through the window, he was fast asleep!

10 — Next morning, a little girl called Helen walked into the toy shop. It was Helen's birthday and she had come to choose a doll's house. Helen and her mummy were quite poor, so Helen knew she couldn't choose a big house.

However, Helen didn't like any of the big houses as much as she liked a very small one.

"I'll take that one, please," she said.

Can you see which house Helen was pointing to? Yes! It was the one where Harvey was staying!

11 — Helen took the doll's house home and set it in her bedroom. You can guess how surprised she was when the door opened, and out came Harvey!

"Goodness! Who are you?" gasped Helen.

12 — Harvey was surprised to see Helen. He thought he was still in the toy shop! However, he explained how he came to be in the doll's house.

"I'm sorry if I startled you," said Harvey. "I was only staying there one night."

"You can stay for ever, if you like," said Helen. "I don't mind."

Harvey was so pleased to hear that!

"Hurrah!" he cheered. "This little house is just right for me!"

So Harvey found a new home after all — in Helen's doll's house! And Helen was delighted to have someone to talk to and play with. But she didn't tell anyone about Harvey. That was her own very special secret!

"Jingles"

F is for Frost,
Making everything white.
These patterns were made
By Jack Frost in the night.

R is for River,
All covered with ice.
Now we can go skating,
And won't *that* be nice?

O is for Outdoors,
Where I go to play.
I'm cosily dressed,
For it's so cold today.

S is for Snow.
Just look — Bimbo and me
Have made a fine snowman
That's big as can be.

T 's for Toboggan.
Mine's red, pink and blue.
I *love* to go sledging.
I'm sure *you* do, too!

The Pink Sugar Mouse

1 — It was Christmas Eve. When every-one in the house was asleep, the Pink Sugar Mouse came alive by magic. He jumped from the Christmas Tree.

2 — "Let's have some fun," he called. So, the coloured Ball, the frosted Bell, the Man-in-the-Moon and the glass Peacock leapt on to the "snow".

3 — "I'm going to build a shelter for a snowball fight," said the Mouse. "Well, while you're doing that, we'll make a giant snowball," tinkled the Bell.

4 — The frosted Bell made a little snowball. Then his chums helped him to push it around until, at last, it was too big for them to move any further.

5 — "Pink Sugar Mouse!" called out the glass Peacock. "Look at our snowball!" But there was no sign of him. The tree decorations searched *everywhere*.

6 — Then, quite suddenly, a hole appeared in the giant snowball. And there, scrambling out of the hole, was the Pink Sugar Mouse!

7 — "Oh, dear! That great heap of snow we rolled our snowball over must have been your shelter!" gasped a Ball. "And *I* was inside!" cried the Mouse.

8 — Then the clock on the wall chimed midnight. "Time to go back to the tree," said the Mouse. "Merry Christmas, all," he added, just as the magic wore off.

Baby Crockett

1 — One day, Baby goes to the newsagent's shop to buy comic. However, as he leaves the shop, the wind blow the comic out of his hands.

4 — . . . and lands on Baby! His head bursts through, making our chum look like an elephant! He *does* look funny!

5 — Further along the lane, a chimney swe is loading tools on to his lorry. There is a b of soot, too.

8 — When Baby arrives home, he is very glum. "I *hate* the wind!" he moans. "I've got something to make you happy," smiles Dad.

9 — Mr Crockett hands him a parc When Baby sees what is inside, his ey light up. "Oh, super!" he cries.

— "Oh, no!" gasps Baby. He runs after it,
ut the comic flies into a tree. Our little
chum can't reach it.

3 — Baby decides to go home. In the lane,
there is a bill poster at work. Just then, the
sticky poster blows away . . .

— Next moment, the bag topples
ver and poor Baby is covered with
soot! What a mess he is in!

7 — "I *am* sorry," says the sweep. A lady comes
out. "The wind blew the bag over, but I'll soon
clean you up," she tells the little lad.

10 — Baby dashes to the park. You see, Dad has
given him a kite. "I *love* the wind *now*!" laughs
Baby, as the kite soars high above him.

ONE day, I went to Willow Farm
For tea with Farmer Hay.
He took me to the barn to see
His new-born chicks at play.

The chicks wanted to play a game
They chirped, "What can we do?"
"Here is a little game," I said,
"Especially for you."

"I've hidden eggs for you to find —
One, two, three, four, five, six."

Now see if *you* can spot them, too —
Just like the little chicks!

How to make
Oswald Owl

by **Bimbo**

ASK Mummy for an empty cardboard cylinder, such as the inside tube of a kitchen roll. This is for Oswald's body. Colour it and make a feather pattern on it.

Draw an outline of the owl's face, wings and feet on stiff paper, as shown here. (Notice that the face is drawn on paper that is folded down the middle.) Then colour all the pieces and cut them out.

Now stick the feet, wings and face in position and you have your very own Oswald Owl!

ALL ABOARD!

**with
Pip the Penguin**

Pip has no one to play with, so he goes sledging.

He whizzes down a hill towards a big, hollow log . . .

. . . and scoops up Peter Polar Bear who was sleeping inside!

But now Pip cannot see properly to steer the sledge.

Next moment, the sledge bumps into a tree on the slope . . .

. . . and Cyril Squirrel falls out of the tree, on to Pip's sledge.

Now the sledge speeds towards a tunnel in the snow.

The tunnel is where Henry Hare stays. He is scooped up, too!

The sledge comes to a stop at the foot of the hill.

Pip is happy, because he is not lonely any more.

You see, thanks to his runaway sledge, he now has plenty of playmates!

Billy and his Boats

1 — Billy Parker met his chum, Pam, one day. "Would you like to come and help me sail my new boats?" he asked.

2 — "Yes, please!" said Pam. The two friends went into a nearby park. Soon, they had blown up the paddling pool which Billy had brought with him. "This is super fun," laughed Billy.

3 — Suddenly, a duck waddled up and decided to have a peck at the pool to see if it tasted nice. The pool burst with a *"bang!"* "Oh, no!" cried Peter.

4 — The chums took the boats into Farmer Green's yard. "This horse-trough can't burst!" laughed Billy. "Here's Farmer Green," said Pam.

5 — Molly, the farmer's horse, had been working hard. As soon as she reached the trough she began to drink . . . and drink . . . and drink. "She's going to drink *all* the water!" cried Billy.

6 — "I can't sail my boats any-where," said Billy, crossly. "I may as well go home." He said good-bye to Pam.

7 — Later that day, Billy had a bath. He took his toy boats with him and put them in the water. Then he put on his captain's hat.

8 — "Ho-ho!" laughed Billy. "At *last,* I have found somewhere I can sail my boats in peace. Ahoy, there!" he cried, looking at his boats through a telescope.

M is for MOUSE. See her scamper about. She's looking for crumbs, since the cat has gone out!

N is for NEWT, coloured green and so small, Who hides in the grass and is not seen at all!

O for the OTTER. She just loves to play, By splashing around in the water all day.

R for RACCOON. Look! His manners are good. Before he has dinner, he washes his food!

S is for SQUIRREL. He hides nuts away To eat when he wakes one cold winter's day

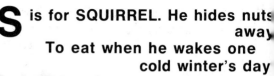

W for WOLF. When he goes on the prowl, He throws back his head and gives out a big howl!

X is a CROSS. And it's sometimes a KISS — The love birds of Africa like doing this!

×